Coloring by:

The Advent STORYBOOK

COLORING BOOK

**CHASING
HOPE**
PRESS

We hope you enjoy *The Advent Storybook Coloring Book* this season!

The coloring pages and ornaments match the 25 stories found in *The Advent Storybook: 25 Bible Stories Showing Why Jesus Came*. As your family travels through ancient history, tracing God's recurring promise to rescue us, we hope these daily activities enhance your journey. In addition to keeping little hands busy during story time, the coloring pages and custom ornaments serve as visual reminders of each story and the truth it shares. (As a bonus, your child receives mini art lessons through hands-on interaction with the artwork!)

Together, let's remember the hope and light Jesus brings to us all.

Merry Christmas!
Laura Richie & Ian Dale

We would love to see your family's artwork!
Tag #adventstorybook on Facebook, Instagram, or Twitter.

THE ADVENT STORYBOOK COLORING BOOK
Published by Chasing Hope Press

Copyright © 2020 Chasing Hope Press
Illustrations © 2020 Ian Dale
Book design by Ian Dale

ISBN: 978-1-7357220-0-9
eISBN: 978-1-7357220-1-6
ISBN for *The Advent Storybook*: 978-0-8307-7608-5

First Edition 2020

A Perfect Life Ends

Genesis 2-3

DAY
3

Sacrifices

Genesis 22

DAY 7

Jacob's Family
Genesis 27-30, 37, 39

DAY
9

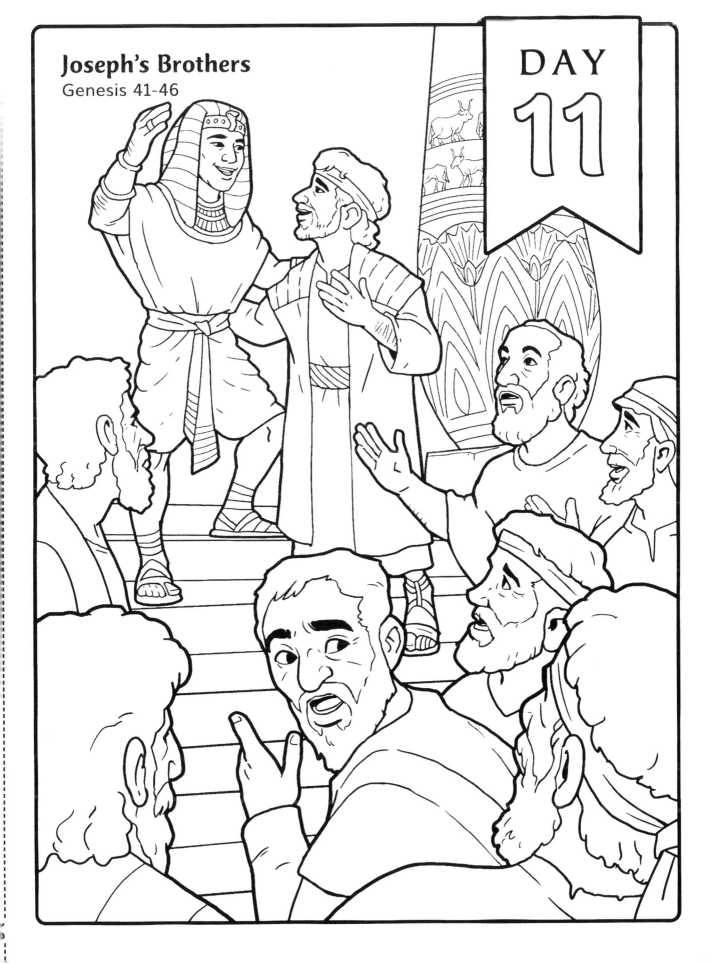

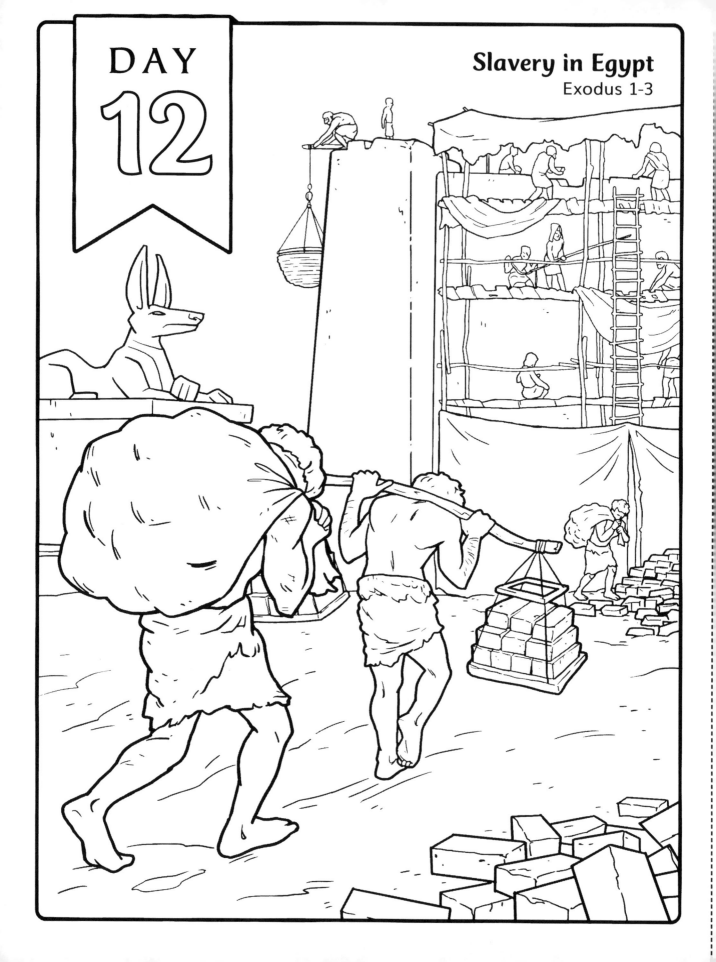

DAY
14

Passover and Rescue
Exodus 12-15

Covenant
Exodus 19-20

DAY 15

Shepherd and King
1 Samuel 16, 17; 2 Samuel 7

DAY
18

Jonah
Jonah 1-4

The Suffering Hero
Isaiah 53

DAY
19

DAY
20

Promises of Grace
Isaiah 55, 65

DAY 22

Daniel and the Kingdom
Daniel 1-2

Humbled Kings

Daniel 3-6

The Promised Son
Matthew 1-2; Luke 1-2

DAY
25

Come and see
the Promised Son!

Daily Advent Ornaments

The 25 ornaments could adorn a Christmas tree or attach to a banner, board, or section of your wall. My kids love decorating the Christmas tree with handmade ornaments. I'm excited to watch how the coloring of each child progresses year to year, and I look forward to pulling out these ornaments and remembering our special Advent seasons in the years to come.

We'd love to see your family's artwork! Tag #adventstorybook on Facebook, Twitter, or Instagram.

SUPPLIES:

Scissors

Coloring materials (crayons, colored pencils, markers, or washable paint)

Ribbon or string

Hole punch

Optional—Laminator with laminating sheets

INSTRUCTIONS:

1. Cut out each ornament.

2. Have child color the front. Write child's name and the Advent year on back.

3. Optional—Laminate to preserve ornaments as keepsakes.

4. Use hole punch then thread hole with ribbon.

5. Decorate your Christmas tree, board, or banner with the daily ornament as the story is read.

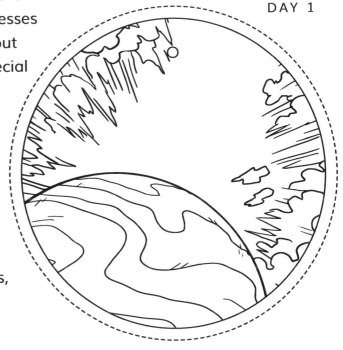

DAY 1

DAY 2

DAY 1

Creation

DAY 2

A Perfect Life

DAY 3

DAY 4

DAY 5

DAY 6

....
NAME

....
YEAR

DAY 3
A Perfect Life Ends

....
NAME

....
YEAR

DAY 4
The Flood

....
NAME

....
YEAR

DAY 5
Abram and God's Promise

....
NAME

....
YEAR

DAY 6
A Promise Kept

DAY 7

DAY 8

DAY 9

DAY 10

....
NAME

....
YEAR

DAY 7
Sacrifices

....
NAME

....
YEAR

DAY 8
Abraham and Isaac

....
NAME

....
YEAR

DAY 9
Jacob's Family

....
NAME

....
YEAR

DAY 10
Joseph's Trials

DAY 11

DAY 12

DAY 13

DAY 14

....
NAME

....
YEAR

DAY 11
Joseph's Brothers

....
NAME

....
YEAR

DAY 12
Slavery in Egypt

....
NAME

....
YEAR

DAY 13
Moses and the Plagues

....
NAME

....
YEAR

DAY 14
Passover and Rescue

DAY 15

DAY 16

DAY 17

DAY 18

....
NAME

....
YEAR

DAY 15
Covenant

....
NAME

....
YEAR

DAY 16
Ruth

....
NAME

....
YEAR

DAY 17
Shepherd and King

....
NAME

....
YEAR

DAY 18
Jonah

DAY 19

DAY 20

DAY 21

DAY 22

....
NAME

....
YEAR

DAY 19
The Suffering Hero

....
NAME

....
YEAR

DAY 20
Promises of Grace

....
NAME

....
YEAR

DAY 21
Josiah

....
NAME

....
YEAR

DAY 22
Daniel and the Kingdom

DAY 23

DAY 24

DAY 25

....
NAME

....
YEAR

DAY 23
Humbled Kings

....
NAME

....
YEAR

DAY 24
Gabriel's Good News

....
NAME

....
YEAR

DAY 25
The Promised Son

Easily print additional copies of
The Advent Storybook Coloring Book!

Perfect for families with multiple children or for church ministries, the electronic PDF download offers unlimited printing for household members or individual churches with a one-time purchase!*

Download today at
ChasingHopePress.com

CHASING HOPE | PRESS

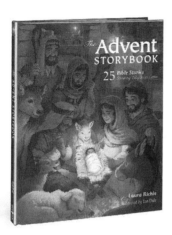
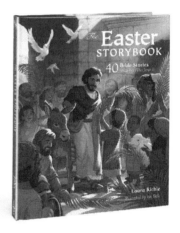

Made in the USA
Middletown, DE
24 October 2021

50883107R00028